WERE YOU THERE?

SERMONS FOR LENT AND EASTER

By Erich H. Heintzen

CONCORDIA PUBLISHING HOUSE   •   SAINT LOUIS, MISSOURI

Dedicated to

the Memory of My Father
and to the Students of the
University Lutheran Chapel,
Champaign, Illinois

CONTENTS

WERE YOU THERE

When He Was Betrayed?

*A*nd *while He yet spake, lo, Judas, one of the twelve, came, and with him a great multitude with swords and staves, from the chief priests and elders of the people. Now he that betrayed Him gave them a sign, saying, Whomsoever I shall kiss, that same is He; hold Him fast. And forthwith he came to Jesus, and said, Hail, Master; and kissed Him. And Jesus said unto him, Friend, wherefore art thou come? Then came they, and laid hands on Jesus, and took Him. And, behold one of them which were with Jesus stretched out his hand, and drew his sword, and struck a servant of the high priest's, and smote off his ear. Then said Jesus unto him, Put up again thy sword into his place: for all they that take the sword shall perish with the sword. Thinkest thou that I cannot now pray to My Father, and He shall presently give Me more than twelve legions of*

angels? But how then shall the Scriptures be ful-
filled, that thus it must be? In that same hour said
Jesus to the multitudes, Are ye come out as against
a thief with swords and staves for to take Me? I sat
daily with you teaching in the temple, and ye laid
no hold on Me. But all this was done, that the
Scriptures of the prophets might be fulfilled. Then
all the disciples forsook Him, and fled. — Matt.
26:47-56 (especially vv. 48, 49).

We who live in this age of the jet plane, tele-
vision, and deep-freeze — what possible connection
can we have with something that happened 2,000
years ago in the days of chariots, togas, and torch-
lights? Our relation to the distant past may on the
surface seem hazy and remote. Actually, we are
more closely bound up with the past than we sometimes think. This is true in a unique way of our relation to the suffering and death of our Lord Jesus
Christ. The very fact that we commonly say "our"
Lord Jesus is evidence that we know and feel this
connection.

During these special midweek Lenten services,
let us try to bring our connection with the suffering
and death of our Lord into sharper focus. Let us
endeavor to recapture for ourselves, and to make
plain to others, the relevance of the Passion to our
time, using the searching theme, "Were You There?"
This evening we ask:

WERE YOU THERE WHEN HE WAS BETRAYED?

8

I

Let us see who was there.

Judas was there. Judas, the man from Kerioth, was one of the twelve men chosen by Jesus to be His disciples. Jesus loved him as much as He loved the others; in fact, Judas held a special office in the group: he was the treasurer. But the Scripture also tells us Judas was a thief. Greed, covetousness, finally drove him to betray his Lord to His enemies for 30 pieces of silver — not a large sum. The text briefly describes the actual betrayal in the Garden of Gethsemane: "And while He yet spake, lo, Judas, one of the twelve, came, and with him a great multitude with swords and staves, from the chief priests and elders of the people. Now he that betrayed Him gave them a sign, saying, Whomsoever I shall kiss, that same is He; hold Him fast. And forthwith he came to Jesus, and said, Hail, Master; and kissed Him. And Jesus said unto him, Friend, wherefore art thou come? Then came they, and laid hands on Jesus, and took Him." (Vv. 47-50)

The question, How could Judas, who had lived and walked and talked with the Savior, do such a thing? is perhaps not so very difficult to answer. He had a special weakness and gave in to it from time to time. Finally, we read, Satan entered into his heart and maneuvered him into striking the fatal bargain. Bitter remorse later on did not help Judas, but drove him to hopeless despair and self-murder — "he went out and hanged himself." Judas did not realize that when he first gave in to temptation and

9

ignored Christ, he thereby placed the noose around his neck. Later events only helped to tighten the noose. It is an old, old story with men.

Look into the shadows of Gethsemane again. You will see that the chief priests and elders of the people were there. These were the people who gladly paid Judas to betray Jesus to them in the Garden. Why did they hate Jesus so? Why did they want Him out of the way? Again, the answer is not difficult. They were jealous of Him. They resented and feared his rising popularity with the people. "The world is gone after him," they cried frantically (John 12:19). Resentment, envy, jealousy so overwhelmed their hearts that they plotted the death of Jesus and looked for someone to "put the finger" on Him. There is added shame here because these were the religious leaders, churchmen, who claimed to be God's spokesmen.

The chief priests and elders and Judas were the chief conspirators in the betrayal. But others were indirectly involved. There was the mob of temple police, henchmen and hangers-on, who came with swords and sticks or brickbats. For the most part, they did not know what it was all about. They probably did not care. They were blindly following their leaders. They unthinkingly helped add to the suffering of the innocent Christ.

The disciples were there. Although they had nothing directly to do with betraying Jesus, they did not help Him either. Simon Peter drew his sword to defend his Lord by force. On behalf of Jesus,

10

Peter cut off the right ear of the servant of the high priest. This was misguided, fanatical zeal at its worst. Jesus rebuked His disciple and healed His enemy. Then Peter and the other disciples, filled with bewilderment and fear, forsook Him and fled.

II

Now, let's for a moment forget *who* was there and consider *what* was there — what was in the hearts and minds of these people, what were their attitudes and motives. And what we find there is not so very strange to us today.

There was greed and covetousness that betrayed Jesus. We may call it materialism, that is, an undue regard for money and material things. It is the spirit that puts things before principles, that puts success and the physical comforts of life before the love of God and His holy will. When a 20th-century disciple of Jesus Christ gives up something of Christ in his business, social, or school life to get something from the world, he is betraying Christ for a price. Can you say that you have never at any time in your life come to terms with the world at Christ's expense? No? Then you were there in the garden.

What else was there? There was envy and jealousy that betrayed Christ. Have you been envious or jealous of anyone in such a way that you begrudged the other person what he had? Disliked and perhaps even secretly hated that person? If so, then you were there in the garden. Whatever hurts one of God's children hurts Him, too.

There was blind following of worldly-minded leaders that helped betray Jesus. Many in the mob were just "following the crowd." Have you ever thoughtlessly "followed the crowd" in something that you later felt was an insult and offense to Christ? If so, then you were there in the garden. Remember, before following the crowd, know where the crowd is going.

There was also misguided zeal and fear-inspired faithlessness at the betrayal of Jesus. Think! Have you ever attempted to defend Christ, if not by physical violence, then by force of the sharp word, or by a loveless attack upon His enemies? Or have you ever for fear of ridicule "clammed up" so that it amounted to forsaking Him and fleeing? If so, then you were in the garden with him that night. In St. Mark's account of the betrayal special mention is made of a certain young man that followed Jesus. When the arresting party tried to seize him, he fled, leaving his clothes clutched in their hands. The young man is not identified, his name is a blank. Why, I don't know. But I wonder whether God has not left it blank so that each of us might see himself in that young man and write his own name there.

Yes, in some way or other we disciples of today can see ourselves in the behavior of all those who were with Him in the garden in the night in which He was betrayed. We cannot feel smug as we read the history of the passion of our Lord. You were there. I was there. And if we were there, we too are responsible for what went on there. This is what the writer of the hymn says when he writes:

> My burden in Thy Passion,
> Lord, hast Thou borne for me,
> For it was my transgression
> Which brought this woe on Thee.

III

And this brings us to Him who was betrayed in the Garden, Jesus, the Lamb of God, that taketh away the sin of the world.

And in Him, too, we see ourselves intimately related to what took place in the garden and in the judgment hall and on Calvary. We are, then, not only connected with the betrayers but also with Him who was betrayed. This is what Isaiah means when he says: "Surely He hath borne our griefs and carried our sorrows. . . . But He was wounded for our transgressions; He was bruised for our iniquities; the chastisement of our peace was upon Him, and with His stripes we are healed. All we like sheep have gone astray; we have turned every one to his own way; and the Lord hath laid on Him the iniquity of us all." (Is. 53:4-6)

In these words the prophet connects the whole human race with the suffering of Christ, because Christ is the sinner's Substitute. So we were "there" in the garden in the person of Christ, our Substitute. A substitute is one who takes another's place, does for another what that one is unable to do. By His perfect obedience to His Father's will He kept God's will for us. And more, with His innocent suffering and death He paid for the sins of those who made Him suffer. As He in the garden healed the ear of the servant of the high priest, His enemy, so has He cleansed us from our transgressions and restored us to life and true sonship with God our Father.

It is, then, in Him alone that we find the power today to overcome those sinful attitudes and motives that still beset the world. How often covetousness, jealousy, envy, misguided zeal, and fear still come between us and our God and between us and our fellow men in home, in business, in politics, in school! But if He has atoned for our sin, He will also help us to overcome our weaknesses. "For we have not an High Priest which cannot be touched with the feeling of our infirmities; but was in all points tempted like as we are, yet without sin. Let us therefore come boldly before the throne of grace, that we may obtain mercy and find grace to help in time of need." (Heb. 4:15-16)

By His matchless mercy our sins against Him in the Garden have been forgiven us. God for Jesus' sake remembers them no more. We are His own forever. We look with eager hope to see Him again in glory, and to share His fellowship there. Take His precious promise to heart once again: "Where I am, there shall also My servant be." Amen.

WERE YOU THERE

When He Was Denied?

*T*hen took they Him, and led Him, and brought Him into the high priest's house. And Peter followed afar off. And when they had kindled a fire in the midst of the hall, and were set down together, Peter sat down among them. But a certain maid beheld him as he sat by the fire, and earnestly looked upon him, and said, This man was also with Him. And he denied Him, saying, Woman, I know Him not. And after a little while another saw him, and said, Thou art also of them. And Peter said, Man, I am not. And about the space of one hour after another confidently affirmed, saying, Of a truth this fellow also was with Him; for he is a Galilean. And Peter said, Man, I know not what thou sayest. And immediately, while he yet spake, the cock crew. And the Lord turned, and looked upon Peter. And Peter remembered the word of the Lord, how He had said unto *him, Before the cock crow, thou shalt deny Me thrice. And Peter went out, and wept bitterly.* — Luke 22:54-62.

It is possible to view the tragic drama of Christ's suffering and death, from Gethsemane to Calvary, and be filled with nothing more than pity and sorrow for the bruised and bleeding Christ. That would be much the same as watching a sad play or movie, having a good cry, and then going unconcerned about our business. And that would be a tragedy.

It is our purpose during these midweek Lenten services to try to erase as much as possible the idea of actors and audience as we consider the Passion, and to see ourselves involved as participants in the divine drama. For what we see is really the acting out of the drama of the world's redemption, and that includes us all. We are essentially in the cast — not in the audience.

Therefore, we have chosen the theme, "Were You There?" This evening we ask

WERE YOU THERE WHEN HE WAS DENIED?

I

Let us see. After the flight of the disciples from the Garden where they saw their Master betrayed, Peter was drawn back. He followed the mob and the bound Prisoner at a safe distance to the palace of the high priest. There was another disciple who returned after his first flight. That was John, who was for some reason known about the high priest's palace. It was John who got Peter into the courtyard of the palace. Then the two were apparently separated. It was chilly in the early morning hours, and Peter warmed himself by the fire in the hall. This was the setting for his threefold denial of his Lord. The text gives us the details of this memorable moment in simple, unadorned language: "But a certain maid beheld him as he sat by the fire, and earnestly looked upon him, and said, This man was also with Him. And he denied Him, saying, Woman, I know Him not. And after a little while another saw him, and said, Thou art also of them. And Peter said, Man, I am not. And about the space of one hour after another confidently affirmed, saying, Of a truth this fellow also was with Him; for he is a Galilean. And Peter said, Man, I know not what thou sayest. And immediately, while he yet spake, the cock crew." (Vv. 56-60)

Second to the tragedy of the betrayal by Judas in the garden is this denial by Peter in the palace of the high priest. In one way, it is even more shameful. The traitor, as far as we know, had never made any special claims of superior loyalty to the Master, but Peter certainly had. On several occasions he had vigorously proclaimed his undying allegiance to Jesus. Even in the face of the Master's warning, Peter avowed, "Though *all* men shall be offended because of Thee, yet will I *never* be offended" (Matt. 26:33). That was going out pretty far on the limb. But hear this same disciple again: "Lord, I am ready

to go with Thee, both into prison and to death"
(Luke 22:33). Later, after he was converted and
strengthened by Jesus, he was ready. But not yet.
In the high priest's palace, Peter was ready only to
deny Jesus in order to save himself from prison and
death.

Here we see Peter, the "rock" man. But he is
a rock with chinks and cracks in it. Only in Christ
was he truly a rock. Apart from Christ he is crum-
bling sandstone. Yet, while Peter was vehemently
denying Him, He was willingly enduring the insults
and the shame for the sake of truth and for the
salvation of Peter and all like him.

II

As we look back over the scene of Peter's denial,
we can clearly see the several stages of his great sin.

First, there were good intentions. But good intentions based on the flimsy foundations of human
pride. Someone has said that "the road to hell is
paved with good intentions." Good intentions are
no better than the spirit which is behind them. And
Peter's spirit was one of spiritual cocksureness. He
thought himself so much better than others in his
relation to Christ. Others might fail Christ; Peter,
never!

When you heard of a neighbor or fellow Christian
who in a moment of weakness fell headlong into sin,
did you ever ask, "How could he ever do a thing
like that?" Was there perhaps behind that question
this thought, "I'd never do a thing like that"?

18

Watch it! That's the same spirit that tripped up Peter.

Another step in Peter's denial was his stubborn refusal to listen to the warnings of Jesus. Jesus similarly warns us through His Word :"Let him that thinketh he standeth take heed lest he fall" (1 Cor. 10:12). Again, "Watch ye and pray, lest ye enter into temptation" (Mark 14:38). Yet, how often we fail to listen. We don't say it, but we think something like this: "Yes, I heard you Lord. But I know what I'm doing. I can take care of myself." Do you know, that's just what Peter thought!

Then there was Peter's association with the wrong people. Whatever it was that brought him back, it was not to help Jesus. When he was recognized, Peter became panic-stricken. In order to save himself, he tried to dissociate himself from Jesus and to identify himself with His enemies. He began to curse and to swear. It was as much as to say, "Look, boys, I'm one of you." Many others who merely meant to warm themselves at the enemy's fire have gotten themselves badly burned.

But not all denials of our Lord are as direct as Peter's was. Silence may also be eloquent. The other disciples in a way were in this too. They hid and were silent. Today, too, Christ is denied and pained by too many silent Christians in the world. Are some of us among them?

Finally, we can see the progressiveness of sin, climaxed by the shameful rejection of Christ by one who promised to go with Him into prison and to death. When you take the first step, although a small step, in dissociating yourself from Christ, you never know where it will end. Among people you know, possibly with whom you were confirmed, are some who are no longer among the disciples of the Lord. But their defection and ultimate denial was no doubt a gradual process. How is it with you? In which direction are you going? Toward Christ, or away from Him? Face this question honestly tonight.

If you can see yourself anywhere along the way in the stages of Peter's denial — and who of us can say he can't? — then you were there with Peter in those dark shadows of the high priest's palace. Let us make no mistake about it, it's no different just because the spirit of denial is found in us today. The sin of denying the Lord knows no one age or era. The sin that wounded Jesus and which He bore is inherent in the human heart the world over. "By one man (Adam) sin entered into the world, and death by sin; and so death passed upon all men, for that all have sinned" (Rom. 5:12). Yes, we — you and I — were there with Peter.

III

But the incident of the denial does not end so tragically as did that of the betrayal. After Peter's third disavowal we read: "And immediately, while he yet spake, the cock crew. And the Lord turned and looked upon Peter. And Peter remembered the word of the Lord, how He had said unto him, Before the cock crow, thou shalt deny Me thrice. And Peter went out and wept bitterly." (Vv. 60-62)

The love of Jesus did not abandon His faithless disciple, but searched him out. Perhaps it was while Jesus was being led from one part of the building to another that He caught Peter's eye. When Peter looked into the eyes of the Lord, he saw rebuke and hurt, but also pity and forgiveness. In the eyes of Jesus, Peter saw himself as he was, and he also saw once again who Jesus was. We know that the Lord not only forgave Peter, but later also reinstated him into discipleship, drawing from him a threefold profession of love, though now spoken in the spirit of humble faith.

What you see here of Jesus' forgiving love is also for you. For you, too, share in the blessings of His Passion, forgiveness and pardon from all your sin — also the sin of denial. If you were there in Peter's denial, you are also included in Jesus's forgiveness. Have you received it, made it your own, by faith?

What shall we do in the light of His matchless love?

Let us from now on deny ourselves, not Him. This is true discipleship: "If any man will come after Me, let him deny himself, and take up his cross and follow Me. For whosoever will save his life shall lose it: and whosoever will lose his life for My sake shall find it" (Matt. 16:24-25). This is a paradox. But it is the paradox of Paradise.

Yes, let us deny ourselves, and confess Him. Let us confess Him for our own happiness. He tells us again today: "Whosoever therefore shall confess Me before men, him will I confess also before My Father which is in heaven. But whosoever shall deny Me before men, him will I also deny before My Father which is in heaven." (Matt. 10:32-33)

Let us confess Him that others may thereby be brought to Him. What He expected of Peter, He also expects of you tonight: "Ye shall be witnesses unto Me" (Acts 1:8). To deny Him before men is to deny Him *to* men, to hide the Door to heaven from men.

But by our confession of Him we also *strengthen one another*. That is as it should be in the church. Looking ahead just prior to His denial, Jesus said to Peter: "Satan hath desired to have you, that he may sift you as wheat. But I have prayed for thee, that thy faith fail not; and when thou art converted, *strengthen thy brethren*" (Luke 22:31-32). Thus we, too, are to strengthen and encourage each other by our mutual witnessing to our Lord's power and love. Let's remember this: if the church is to be a power without, it must be strong within. Are you strengthening your brothers and sisters in the faith?

One last glance at the lonely, troubled figure in the courtyard. Fear moved Peter to try to make friends with the world that night. In a wider sense, you and I crave and seek recognition in this world. However, in the light of eternity is it not, after all, a small thing whether we are acknowledged by the world? Our chief aim in life is rather this: to confess our Lord faithfully, to be of help to one another, to stand with Him one day before the throne of His

Father in heaven and receive His blessed commendation: "Well done, thou good and faithful servant . . . enter thou into the joy of thy Lord." (Matt. 25:21)

Lord, look on me as You once looked on Peter — before it is too late! Amen.

WERE YOU THERE

When He Was Accused?

And the whole multitude of them arose, and led Him unto Pilate. And they began to accuse Him, saying, We found this fellow perverting the nation, and forbidding to give tribute to Caesar, saying that he himself is Christ a king. And Pilate asked Him, saying, Art thou the King of the Jews? And He answered him and said, Thou sayest it. Then said Pilate to the chief priests and to the people, I find no fault in this man. And they were the more fierce, saying, He stirreth up the people, teaching throughout all Jewry, beginning from Galilee to this place. — Luke 23:1-5.

After His betrayal in the garden, the Lord was led away by His captors to the palace of the high priest. Here He was detained and humiliated in the quarters of Annas, the former high priest, until the

Sanhedrin, the highest Jewish tribunal, could be called together. Soon the members of the council, who had been routed from their beds for this extraordinary and illegal session, were in their places. Under the scheming leadership of Caiaphas the high priest, Jesus was accused and condemned. And then "the whole multitude of them arose, and led Him unto Pilate."

Let's take a brief look at this multitude. There are the chief priests and elders, members of the Sanhedrin, and doubtless also some of their henchmen and hangers-on — possibly a hundred or more men. But because of the unique nature and deeper significance of the occasion the number is infinitely larger. In fact, the whole human race is rightly seen in this multitude which accused the innocent Christ. We shall see that we and all men share in that sin against the Lord. To sharpen our awareness of this tragic truth we put the question this evening:

WERE YOU THERE WHEN HE WAS ACCUSED?

I

What were the accusations brought against Jesus?

Before the Jewish council the Lord was accused on religious grounds. It was difficult to find witnesses to testify against Jesus. But finally two false witnesses appeared who accused Him of having said something about destroying the great temple of

Herod and rebuilding it again in three days. This was a distortion of a statement of Jesus concerning His death and resurrection on the third day. But the most serious charge was lodged against Him by the high priest Caiaphas, who in desperation abandoned his role as moderator and turned prosecutor. He drew from Jesus the blessed confession that He was the Son of God and for that accused Him of blasphemy, of insulting God. The Council then condemned Jesus to death — the penalty for blasphemy. Jesus was then hustled off to the headquarters of Pilate, for the Jews needed the sanction of the Roman government to carry out the death penalty.

However, before the governor Pontius Pilate, the representative of the Roman government, the accusations are quite different. "And they began to accuse Him, saying, We found this fellow perverting the nation, and forbidding to give tribute to Caesar, saying that he himself is Christ a king." Here the charges are based on alleged crimes against the state. We see how calculatingly the accusations are tailored to suit the occasion. That the charges were unjust and ridiculous need not be discussed. They were a combination of outright lies and half-truths. Even the Roman governor did not take them seriously. He was not deceived by this strange, sudden interest of the Jews in the welfare of the Roman state. And after briefly questioning Jesus about His alleged kingship, the governor flatly declared, "I find no fault in him." As a matter of fact, these words become a refrain that is heard again and again throughout the trial of Jesus — indeed down through history.

The arraignment of the Holy One did not end with this trial before Caiaphas and Pilate. In the turbulent centuries which followed, down to this very day, the innocent Christ has been accused of many things. Some call Him a deceiver; others, a dreamer. Communism brands His blessed teachings as dangerous to the people.

But these charges and criticisms, today as then, collapse under the sheer weight of their own falseness. After all these years His standing challenge, "Which of you convinceth Me of sin?" still silences maligning mouths (John 8:46). And those who are called upon to judge Him, and who like Pilate may not believe in Him or follow Him, are compelled to repeat the verdict of the Roman: "I find no fault in him."

But we don't need that endorsement. We believe Him — believe Him because He has through the Gospel call spoken to us with an overpowering persuasiveness, as has no one else. He has fulfilled His promise to us, "Ye shall *know* the truth. . . ." This we have experienced.

II

Now let us look more closely at Jesus' accusers.

We see there first of all the chief priests, the elders, and other members of the Sanhedrin. These were personally and directly involved in these shameful accusations against the Son of God. But they do not stand alone. The sin of accusing God and His Son is a universal sin; it is a sin of all mankind.

Adam first accused God in the garden. After his violation of God's will, Adam accused God of having been responsible. Adam blamed not only Eve; he blamed God, too, when he said, "The woman whom *Thou* gavest to be with me, she gave me of the tree, and I did eat" (Gen. 3:12). Later on Job's wife accused God for their misfortune. She urged Job to curse God and die. During the wanderings of Israel in the wilderness the people whom God had miraculously led through the Red Sea and supplied with food, again and again accused God of having led them out of Egyptian bondage to rot in the wilderness.

Yes, the scene of the innocent Christ accused by the people of His day is the most tragic, but it is one of many incidents in which man has dared to accuse his Maker and his Redeemer.

The chief priests and the elders were there. Adam was there. The Israelites were there. Were you there — when Jesus was accused?

Have you ever felt, particularly during times of trouble or disappointment, that God isn't giving you a square deal? Have you ever prayed faithfully for something dear to your heart and then after waiting and waiting blamed God for not hearing your prayer? Do you ever feel that Christ is asking far too much of you — of your time, of your talent, of your treasure? What is all this, if it is not accusing God and the Savior of being incompetent and unfaithful? And if we accuse God, in what way are we any different from those who unjustly accused His Son our Lord before the tribunal of Caiaphas and the court of Pilate? If we accuse God, then we were there with them.

We were there also because of our frequent offenses against the Eighth Commandment, "Thou shalt not bear false witness against thy neighbor." Whatever hurts our neighbor hurts God's Son. We cannot confine the implications of this word of God simply to courtroom witnessing. Luther explains it this way: "We should fear and love God that we may not deceitfully belie, betray, slander, nor defame our neighbor. . . ." For every person who has been falsely accused in court there are a thousand who have been slandered by malicious gossip over the bridge table, over cocktails, or over the back fence. Unfounded rumors and misinformation thoughtlessly repeated, and usually embellished, amount to slanderous accusations and are all part of that hideous sin which did not even spare the innocent Christ. And those who are always ready to lend a willing ear to these accusations are equally guilty.

Yes, if we are honest, we can't stand off tonight and simply condemn those who accused Jesus, but must rather confess an equal guilt and take our place among them.

III

But let us look once more at the Accused.

Whom do we see? An innocent man. Pilate condemned him, but declared Him innocent. But more.

He is the sinless Son of God. He, the accused and the judged, is the Judge of all. As He stated before the high priest and the council: "Hereafter shall ye see the Son of Man sitting on the right hand of power, and coming in the clouds of heaven" (Matt. 26:64). He is also the Savior of the world, as He said: "The Son of Man came not to be ministered unto, but to minister, and to give His life a ransom for many" (Matt. 20:28). It was His sinless, holy life that was laid on the scales to outbalance the weight of the world's sin — our sin.

All our heinous and damning sins of false accusation against God's Son and the sons of men have by His precious blood been wiped away. "In Him we have redemption through His blood, even the forgiveness of sins" (Col. 1:14). It is in the very righteousness of the Accused that the accusers find the righteousness with which to stand before God.

Behold, what manner of love God hath bestowed upon us — once accusers of His Son — that we should be called the sons of God!

Knowing this, we can only look with horror upon the sin of false and loveless accusation in all its forms. Let us guard our minds and our lips that we speak no evil against our neighbor and so wound Christ anew. We can be content only with evermore striving to speak the truth and do the truth. Truth, God's truth, is the one thing we need most. That is the Great Indispensable of our lives. Let us be eternally grateful that we have this truth in Him who is the Way, the Truth, and the Life!

30

WERE YOU THERE

When He Was Condemned?

When Pilate saw that he could prevail nothing, but that rather a tumult was made, he took water, and washed his hands before the multitude, saying, I am innocent of the blood of this just person: see ye to it. Then answered all the people, and said, His blood be on us, and on our children. Then released he Barabbas unto them: and when he had scourged Jesus, he delivered Him to be crucified. — Matthew 27:24-26.

It is a terrible thing for a person to be condemned and sentenced to prison for a crime he did not commit. Even if the victim of a miscarriage of justice is later proved innocent and released from prison, the injustice cannot be completely undone. Even though the state makes some financial amends, nothing can restore the years of freedom lost in prison. It must be difficult for one who has been the victim of such injustice to keep from becoming implacably bitter.

In the text for this evening we see an even greater tragedy. This is the condemnation and sentencing to death, not merely of an innocent man, but of the sinless Son of God. Here was no ordinary case of mistaken justice, but a deliberate and calculated plot to thwart justice. Our sense of honesty and fairness revolts at this sickening scene in the Roman praetorium.

But as we look more closely at the people involved in this shameful episode, we know that they do not stand alone. To some degree, all the motives and attitudes that we find at work there are still with us today — hatred, prejudice, false accusations, envy, dishonesty. These sins bind men of today to those men of 2,000 years ago. These things also raise their ugly heads in our hearts and lives. We must constantly battle to keep them under control. Therefore it is not out of place to ask

WERE YOU THERE WHEN HE WAS CONDEMNED?

I

We observe that as Jesus only a short time before was condemned by the church, He is now condemned by the state.

Pilate, the Roman governor, admitted that it was within his arbitrary power to release or to crucify the innocent Christ. In spite of his better judgment, he chose to condemn an innocent man in order to save his own position. He was a politician in the bad sense of that term. With a pathetic show of right he washed his hands before the clamoring mob, saying, "I am innocent of the blood of this just person; see ye to it."

This was not the only instance in which Christ and His church have been condemned by the state. Others soon took Pilate's place. For 300 years the Roman emperors condemned Christ and His followers as persons dangerous to the state. The Christians were hunted down and put to death. The sands of the Roman arena ran red with the blood of these martyrs. In our own times atheistic communism has condemned Christ as dangerous, branding the Christian religion as well as others as "the opiate of the people." Christian altars have been desecrated, churches turned into museums and other public buildings, Christians persecuted and "liquidated." Other examples could be cited to show how in the course of history Pilate's sin, in essence, has been committed again and again.

We rightly abhor all condemnation of Christ by the state. But let us remember that we as Christians in America have a unique responsibility for our government. The relationship of church and state should of course be vitally important to all citizens, particularly to the Christians. If by indifference to our civic duties and responsibilities we permit government to fall into the hands of unscrupulous men so that justice, honesty, fairness, and truth are violated, are we not inviting and abetting the condemnation of everything Christ stands for? Will not the work of the church, the cause of Christ's kingdom, be made more difficult? In many ways, without our thinking, we may become guilty of condemning Christ and His cause, not so much by sins of commission as by sins of omission. In the end, however, is there any real difference?

The condemnation of our Lord by a representative of the Roman state should remind us that we cannot be content scrupulously to avoid condemning Christ. We should the more vigorously preach Him, confess Him in our lives as Christian citizens, and be ready to serve Him in public office, if we have the ability and opportunity.

II

But look again at the Biblical scene. We observe, furthermore, that Christ was condemned not only by an official of the state, but just as much by the people.

When Pilate hypocritically washed his hands of Jesus' blood, the people shouted, "His blood be on us and on our children." A terrible thing to say! On Palm Sunday, a few days before, some of these people doubtless had acclaimed Him with Hosannas. What made them change? "The chief priests and elders persuaded the multitude that they should ask Barabbas, and destroy Jesus" (Matt. 27:20). In their judgment of Jesus the people were influenced, prompted, goaded by others. Their mistake was that they let others do their religious thinking for them.

This is a common mistake. Jesus warns against it. Once when He asked His disciples, "Whom do men say that I the Son of Man am?" He immediately followed with the question, "Whom say ye that I am?" (Matt. 16:13, 15.) We must know Him for ourselves. But our faith in Him, our thinking about Him, must be based on God's Word and not on man's. Some people are guided in their religious thinking by what prominent people think. If a scientist, or movie star, or philosopher, or explorer expounds the subject of religion, many people will go along with it because a very important person has said so. Well-meaning Christians sometimes adopt the same attitude. They believe what they do because their parents or church or pastor teach it. The teaching may be correct, but the teachers are not the ground of faith. Our religious thinking must be based solidly on God's Word. To build otherwise is to court disaster. Remember, the people in Pilate's court condemned Jesus because they let others do their religious thinking for them.

Furthermore, we see in this crowd another common human failing or sin. That is the inclination to judge and condemn our neighbor without just cause. How often don't we misjudge a person's remarks or actions and put the worst construction on them! Or how often don't we listen to prejudiced reports and then condemn! Jesus cautions us: "Judge not, and ye shall not be judged; condemn not, and ye shall not be condemned" (Luke 6:37). He knows what it is to be condemned by cold, loveless, mis-

35

guided judgment. It was also this sin of man that added to His great suffering.

Can we honestly say that we have never had any part in these sins which were involved in the condemnation of our Lord? Surely, our heart tells us we were there. It is only when we admit that we were there, that it was also for our sin that He suffered and died, that we can see Him as our Savior. It is only after we have acknowledged our sin and repented of our sin that we can say of Him, as Paul did, "He loved *me* and gave Himself for *me*" (Gal. 2:20). This means that in Him, by His innocent suffering and death for the sin of all mankind, I too can find pardon and peace. By His condemnation He freed us from condemnation, so that there is now "no condemnation to them which are in Christ Jesus, who walk not after the flesh, but after the Spirit." (Rom. 8:1)

III

How can we explain the magnitude of God's grace in Christ? We of course cannot; we can only wonder at it. But our wonderment must soon give way to the question, Can't I somehow make amends for the sorrow and the pain that sin — my sin — has caused Him? The answer again is: No, *you* never can. *He* has made the atonement for that before God. For this we are forever indebted to Him.

But there are ways in which we can show our grateful love to Him. First, we can watch and pray that we do not in any way condemn Him anew. We can also be patient and forgiving toward those who criticize and judge us mistakenly and unjustly. General Robert E. Lee was once asked by the President what he thought of another officer called Whiting. "Whiting? Why, a very fine officer, Mr. President. One of the ablest men in the army," Lee replied. The President looked surprised. "But don't you know," he continued, "that General Whiting has been saying some very unkind things about you?" "Oh, yes," was the reply, "I knew that. But, Mr. President, you have asked me what I think of General Whiting, not what General Whiting thinks of me." The Christian, like his Lord, when he is reviled, will revile not again.

We can show our love to our Lord by defending those who are unjustly condemned and by speaking the truth one with another. This is the acid test of our love for Christ, namely, our Christian concern for others. No amount of tears over our sin and over the suffering it has caused Christ the Redeemer will mean anything if our love does not go out to those whom He redeemed and who are precious in His sight.

Let us this evening, as we see again the tragic spectacle of the innocent Christ condemned to death for our sins, ask His help to be more loyal to Him and to His church; to speak more boldly and positively in His behalf; and to defend our neighbor when he is unjustly condemned. For in this, too, His blessed word applies: "Inasmuch as ye have done it unto one of the least of these My brethren, ye have done it unto Me. . . ." (Matt. 25:40)

WERE YOU THERE

When He Was Crowned with Thorns?

Then the soldiers of the governor took Jesus into the common hall, and gathered unto Him the whole band of soldiers. And they stripped Him, and put on Him a scarlet robe. And when they had platted a crown of thorns, they put it upon His head, and a reed in His right hand: and they bowed the knee before Him, and mocked Him, saying, Hail, King of the Jews! And they spit upon Him, and took the reed, and smote Him on the head. — Matt. 27:27-30.

The text this evening reminds us of one of the most familiar paintings of the passion of our Lord, the *Ecce Homo*, showing Jesus wearing the crown of thorns. That painful crown platted by the soldiers and pressed into His sacred head has long since disappeared. But there have been others. Throughout the years men have been making their own crowns of thorns, sometimes not realizing what they were doing, and tormenting Christ anew with those crowns.

If this seems strange to you, then simply remember this, that the crown of thorns was just one of the instruments of torture which the soldiers used in their whole sordid game of mocking Christ. It was a symbol of their mocking attitude. And their mockery consisted in this: to treat Jesus as a *king in name only*. That was the essence of their game. And that is the same treatment Christ gets today from so many. They regard him as their king in name only.

Is it possible that we, too, sometimes treat Him that way? Is it possible that we share in this shameful treatment of our Lord, in essence?

WERE YOU THERE WHEN HE WAS CROWNED WITH THORNS?

I

Let us see what went on there. Pontius Pilate's soldiers — and some of them were no doubt the counterpart of our modern "goons" — had heard Jesus claim to be a king. Very well, then, they would now give Him the treatment that befitted such a king! For a king's garment, they put on Him a handy purple robe. For a crown of jewels, they placed on His head a crown of thorns. For a scepter, they put a reed in His hand. For loyal servants, they themselves bowed before Him, saying, "Hail, King of the Jews." Then they spit on Him, and took the reed and struck Him on the head.

Little did they realize what they were doing. Had they realized the truth they would have paled with fear and trembled in terror. For He was King — the King of heaven and earth. The only-begotten Son of God left His heavenly kingdom to be born of the virgin in a stable in Bethlehem. He took upon Himself the form of a servant. But from time to time He gave the people glimpses of His almighty power. He stilled a storm at sea by the power of His word. He fed 5,000 people with the miracle of five barley loaves and two small fish. He called His dead friend Lazarus to life from the tomb where he had lain for four days. And now He had only a few hours before thrown to the ground those who had come to the garden to arrest Him. This was He whom these puny men were mocking and maltreating — the Almighty God in the flesh.

Why, then, does He permit these coarse soldiers to mock Him and crown Him with thorns? The answer is that in these hours the Lord is not openly acting as King, but as Priest. He has laid aside the use of His kingly power in order to make an atonement for the sin of men, even of these men who are making this horrible sport of Him. As our Mediator before God, Jesus is about to bring a sacrifice for our sin, and that sacrifice is to be none other than His own spotless self. The reason why He endures these terrible indignities is that He is the Lamb of God which taketh away the sin of the world. He is here fulfilling the prophecy of old: "He was wounded for our transgressions, He was bruised for our iniquities:

the chastisement of our peace was upon Him; and with His stripes we are healed. All we like sheep have gone astray . . . and the Lord hath laid on Him the iniquity of us all." (Is. 53:5)

And if He was wounded for our transgressions, if by His stripes we were healed, then we were involved in His suffering, we contributed to it. For His suffering was caused by the sin of the human race, of which the sin of our age and of our lives is a part.

II

Were you there when He was crowned with thorns? Now let's see just what this was. This was all part of a more fundamental sin, that of treating Jesus as a king in name only. Don't we all fall into this sin at times? Let's not think here only of unbelievers and hypocrites. Let us think of ourselves who say we take Him seriously when He says: "I am a king. . . . My kingdom is not of this world. . . . To this end was I born, and for this cause came I into the world, that I should bear witness unto the truth. Every one that is of the truth heareth my voice." (John 18:36-37)

Our King says, "If ye continue in My Word, then are ye My disciples indeed; and ye shall know the truth, and the truth shall make you free" (John 8:31-32). How much does God's Word figure in your daily life? Do you read it, study it? Is it important to you? If we neglect His Word, we despise and mock Him. He is not a king to us, but one whom we push aside. What of our attendance at public worship and our attendance at the Lord's Table? Don't we sometimes push Him aside here too? Don't we make of Him a king in name only?

Our King bids us love one another: "A new commandment I give unto you, That ye love one another; as I have loved you, that ye also love one another" (John 13:34). Yet there are those who call Jesus their king and who hate others, who carry long-standing grudges, and will not even talk to others. There are Christian homes which have on the walls plaques reading "Christ is the Head of this house, the Unseen Guest at every meal." But the discussion and strife that rules the hearts in that home show that Christ is there just a king in name only.

Or is Christ truly the King of our money and goods? Is He the King of our pocketbooks? If He were, then the church treasuries would be overflowing. There would not be any crippling deficits. If Christ were really and truly King to all in the area of Christian stewardship, there would be more and greater offerings of love to Him instead of what amounts to a mere tip now and then.

Our King urges us to be fervent in prayer. He says, "All things, whatsoever ye shall ask in prayer, believing, ye shall receive" (Matt. 21:22). Certainly, every Christian prays. But don't we sometimes grow weak in prayer, pray halfheartedly or mechanically, as if it did not make any difference? That is to treat Jesus as a king in name only. All this is even more shameful in our case. The soldiers who knelt before

Him admittedly did not take Jesus seriously as a king. But we say that we do.

Yes, we must admit we were there, and that we have been there again and again.

III

But in spite of all our sins of weakness against our King, in spite of our unworthiness, He forgives us by His grace and keeps us in His kingdom with Him. And He is able to do this because He has overcome all His enemies and our enemies. He reigns in glory now.

> The Head that once was crowned with thorns
> Is crowned with glory now;
> A royal diadem adorns
> The mighty Victor's brow.

Once He "made Himself of no reputation, and took upon Him the form of a servant, and was made in the likeness of men: and being found in fashion as a man, He humbled Himself, and became obedient unto death, even the death of the cross. Wherefore God also hath highly exalted Him, and given Him a name which is above every name: that at the name of Jesus every knee should bow, of things in heaven, and things in earth, and things under the earth; and that every tongue should confess that Jesus Christ is Lord, to the glory of God the Father." (Phil. 2:7-11)

It was this glorification that Jesus foresaw even in the dark hours of His humiliation, and of which He prophesied: "Hereafter shall ye see the Son of Man sitting on the right hand of power, and coming in the clouds of heaven." (Matt. 26:64)

It is this glorious coming to which we look forward with expectant joy. For by the power of His grace we, who have often placed a crown of thorns upon His sacred head, will then receive from His hands a crown of life. Then our hands, which have been cleansed by His precious blood, will be raised only in loving adoration and praise to our eternal Savior-King.

But until He comes in glory, let us serve Him more faithfully as our King in truth, not in name only. Let us praise and proclaim Him by word and deed that others may come to know Him as their Savior and King, that they may share His glory with us when He comes.

WERE YOU THERE

When He Was Crucified?

And there were also two others, malefactors, led with Him to be put to death. And when they were come to the place, which is called Calvary, there they crucified Him, and the malefactors, one on the right hand, and the other on the left. Then said Jesus, Father, forgive them; for they know not what they do. And they parted His raiment, and cast lots. And the people stood beholding. And the rulers also with them derided Him, saying, He saved others; let him save himself, if he be Christ, the chosen of God.

Luke 23:32-35

During the quiet moments of these evening Lenten services we have followed our Lord step by step along the path of His great Passion for our sin. This evening the text brings us to the climax of His suffering, His crucifixion on Calvary.

Now the crucifixion of our Lord may be looked at in two ways: as the people saw it, and as Jesus saw it.

The text states: "The people stood beholding." Most pictures of the crucifixion are painted from that point of view — the view of someone looking at the cross. But a few years ago a member of the University of Illinois department of art took the other point of view. He painted a picture, an extremely striking picture, of the scene on Calvary as it must have appeared to Jesus looking down from the cross. Although not many pictures have been done from this point of view, the text, significantly enough, does this very thing. It gives us Jesus' point of view as He looked down from the cross at the people: "Father, forgive them, for they know not what they do."

These words are the key to the understanding of Calvary. The crucifixion can be rightly understood by us only when we look at it from Jesus' point of view. It is the view of God's forgiving love. "Father, forgive them!" Whom did Jesus see when He spoke these words? Did He see you there?

WERE YOU THERE WHEN HE WAS CRUCIFIED?

I

Jesus included all in His prayer for divine forgiveness. His eyes rested on the soldiers who had nailed Him to the cross. Now they were gambling for his clothing and his seamless coat, reminding us of the prophetic words of David in Psalm 22, "They part My garments among them, and cast lots upon My vesture." No, they did not know what they were doing; they were hardened men, immune, no doubt, to human suffering; this was just another routine matter of Roman justice. But Jesus prayed that they might be forgiven.

From the cross Jesus could see the chief priests, scribes, and elders of the people. These were the ones who had plotted and engineered His crucifixion, and were as guilty as if they had hammered the nails into His hands and feet. Even now they still persist in their mockery and derision, "He saved others; let him save himself, if he be Christ, the chosen of God," again reminding us of the portentous words of Psalm 22. Although these religious leaders had certainly sinned against better knowledge, yet they really did not comprehend the enormity of their crime against the Son of God. Jesus prayed that they, too, might be forgiven.

Then Jesus could see the thieves crucified with Him, one on his left and the other on his right. Both of these criminals at first had ironically joined the chief priests in their jibes against Christ. But after a time the thief on the right, overcome by the strange power of the man on the center cross, repented. And Jesus spoke the word of pardon and peace to him.

And there were others who were not there personally, but whom the forgiving love of Jesus embraced in this prayer. Annas, Caiaphas, Pilate, Herod, Peter and the faithless disciples. He would forgive them, too.

But the eyes of Jesus fell not only on His enemies beneath the cross. "Now there stood by the cross of Jesus His mother, and His mother's sister, Mary the wife of Cleophas, and Mary Magdalene . . . and the disciple (John) . . . whom He loved . . ." (John 19:25-26). Were these His loved ones included in His prayer? After all, these brave souls had taken no active part in this tragedy. Their hearts were breaking with grief. But in the wider sense of Jesus' prayer for forgiveness, they too were included. For on the cross was not merely Mary's son, but God's Son, the only-begotten Son of God who had come into the flesh to redeem all mankind from sin. Behold the Lamb of God which taketh away the sin of the world!

And we who love Him today were there. Our sins helped put Him there. From the crest of Calvary the vision of the Crucified embraced us and all people, for we have all sinned and come short of the glory of God. Let us not be offended to hear this. Rather let us acknowledge our sin and thank Him for including us in His prayer for forgiveness. And ask His help to avoid sin, which once wounded Him and still wounds our fellow men, especially the sin of refusing to forgive others. After being at Calvary with Jesus, can we refuse to give to others what He in His agony prayed His Father to give us? In His name, let us, too, forgive.

II

There is another thing to remember here. Looking at the crucifixion from Jesus' point of view, we see that He not only prayed for our forgiveness, but that He died to *make this forgiveness a reality for us.*

What right does man have to expect God to be merciful to him? The Scripture says, "The soul that sinneth, it shall die" (Ezek. 18:20). Every man who honestly looks into his own soul will have to admit that he is a sinner, that he has in many ways transgressed the holy will of God. His conscience bears witness to this awful truth. But throughout the ages man has tried in hundreds of ways, both crude and refined, to make God favorable to him. The history of religion is for the most part the story of man's ceaseless efforts to placate outraged Justice, attempts of man to build a bridge or a ladder of his own that will lead him back into God's favor. But it is futile for man to try to lift himself out of the mire of his sin by his own bootstraps.

But Christ's view of His crucifixion is that *it* is the answer to mankind's yearning and striving to find peace with God, for by the merits of His own spotless life and of His innocent suffering and death He has paid our debt to God. For His crucified Son's sake God has canceled our sin. "It is finished!" This is the viewpoint of the Crucified as He looks out over the world from Calvary's cross: He hangs there to win forgiveness for them.

It is most important for us that we make Jesus' view of His crucifixion our own. The Apostle Paul was one who understod this well. He had once been in the ranks of those who persecuted Christ and His church. By the forgiving grace of God he had in time been led to see the cross in its true meaning, as Jesus saw it. He saw Jesus hanging there for his sin. And this caused him to make a most striking confession, in which he saw himself not only among the vast number beneath the cross, but with Jesus *on* the cross. He said, "I am crucified *with* Christ." Yes, Paul saw himself on the cross with Christ. This was not presumptuousness on his part, but rather the humble acceptance of the fact that Jesus bore his sin there. And that led Paul to continue: "Nevertheless, I live; yet not I, but Christ liveth in me: and the life which I now live in the flesh I live by the faith of the Son of God, who loved me and gave Himself for me." (Gal. 2:20)

This forgiveness which Christ won for us means new life for us today and every day. For those who have been with Jesus at Calvary, each new day means another day of God's forgiving love. Things may go wrong at home, in school, at work. Serious sickness or sorrow may come our way. Defeat may stare us in the face at every turn. Nevertheless — and Paul reminds us that there is for the Christian always a "nevertheless" — we live! If sin and sorrow and trouble are realities in our lives, then the power of God's forgiveness can be just as great, yes, a greater reality for us. It is the power of God's transforming love in our lives. God does not want you to be without it. He offers it again to you in Christ.

If we want to get the most out of this life and be assured of eternal life, we must first see ourselves crucified with Christ. We must realize that we were there, that we were not only beneath the cross, but *on* the cross with Him. You see, Christ died for the sins of the world, but only when we realize that *we* were there does He become *our* Savior.

> Bane and blessing, pain and pleasure,
> By the Cross are sanctified;
> Peace is there that knows no measure,
> Joys that through all time abide.

WERE YOU THERE

When He Gave the Holy Supper?

And He took bread, and gave thanks, and brake it, and gave it to them, saying, This is My body which is given for you: this do in remembrance of Me. Likewise also the cup after supper, saying, This cup is the new testament in My blood which is shed for you. — Luke 22:19-20.

This is the night in which the Savior was betrayed by one of his own disciples. But prior to this shameful scene the Scripture presents another picture which has become one of the most cherished by Christians of all times: The Last Supper.

The setting is a simple one. Twelve men and their Master are gathered together to observe the traditional Passover meal in an upper room somewhere in Jerusalem. It is the same scene as that being enacted in thousands of Jewish homes that very night.

The festival of the Passover was instituted by God at the time of the exodus of the Israelites from Egypt after four hundred years of slavery. According to God's instructions, the people on the day of their departure killed a lamb "without spot or blemish" and stained their dorways with its crimson blood. They roasted the lamb and ate standing up, ready for travel. That night the avenging angel of God swept across the land of Egypt, leaving the first-born of man and beast lifeless in his wake, but *passing over* the houses of the Israelites whose doorways were marked with the blood of the lamb. A once haughty but humbled Pharaoh now urgently pleaded with this troublesome people to leave with all haste. And six hundred thousand men, besides women and children, began their march to freedom.

God appointed this historic day as a memorial for them. The killing of the Passover lamb every year and the attendant ceremonies of the meal in each home were to be for all generations a vivid reminder of God's mighty deliverance.

This memorial meal it was which our Lord on that first Maundy Thursday was celebrating with His disciples in that upper room. Significantly, it was just during this last Passover meal that He instituted His Holy Supper of the new testament in His blood, to replace that of the old. This is one of the most solemn and sublime moments of all time. Disciples could now enter into a communion with their Lord such as they had never before known. What a blessing for those who were there! Who were they? You recognize Peter, James, John, and the others. Any others? Look at the group again as Jesus saw it in His mind's eye. The Twelve become a multitude as they are joined at His table by countless other disciples down through the ages. What about you?

WERE YOU THERE WHEN HE GAVE HIS HOLY SUPPER?

I

Jesus had you in mind in that upper room. This act, like all the others of His Great Passion, was also for you. He saw you there.

In the midst of the simplicity of the upper room you enter into a mystery of mysteries. At one point during the Passover supper Jesus takes bread, gives thanks, and gives it to His disciples, saying, "This is My body which is given for you: this do in remembrance of Me." Then He takes the cup and gives it to them, saying, "This cup is the new testament in My blood, which is shed for you." Behold, with the bread He gives His body and with the wine, His blood. This is the same body which in a short time will be nailed to the cross, the same blood which will be shed there *for them*, more specifically, as Matthew says, "for the remission of sins." You do not know how this can be. But the Lord's own words assure you that when disciples eat of that bread and drink of that cup, they receive in a supernatural manner the true body and blood of their Lord.

This is to be done also in remembrance of Him. The perpetuation of His Holy Supper as a memorial until the end of time is also an assurance that Jesus has not only the Twelve in mind, but His disciples of all ages, also you. Those first disciples, especially, would need to remember His love and be reassured of His presence. For them there were most difficult days ahead. Jesus was about to withdraw His visible presence from them. What could He give them to support them as they went out into a bitterly hostile world to preach His Gospel of salvation? Nothing less than His own body and blood, which He gave and shed for them on the cross. This would always remind them, as it also reminds you, that His disciples do not stand alone in the world.

As you come to the Lord's Table this evening to commemorate His suffering and death for you, be assured once again that He thought also of you in the upper room when He gave His Holy Supper.

II

Because you were there in His thoughts, He also wants you to enjoy the blessings of His Supper in this your day. What these blessings are is contained in the message of the Lord's Supper.

That message is essentially nothing strange or new in His teaching. The Lord had told His disciples numerous times before, "The Son of Man is come to seek and to save that which was lost" (Luke

19:10). Again, "The Son of Man came not to be ministered unto, but to minister, and to give His life a ransom for many" (Matt. 20:28). Again, "The Son of Man must be killed, and after three days rise again" (Mark 8:31). Yes, all this He had patiently explained to them many times. And now, once more, He tells them that His body would be given and His blood would be shed for their sin. That is pure Gospel, the good news of forgiveness of sins through the death of Jesus Christ. That is the "new testatment," or covenant, in His blood. But it is the same message, essentially, as that of the prophets of old who foretold His coming.

Although the message of the Gospel and of the Lord's Supper is one and the same, the Lord did add something in this Sacrament for you. In addition to His spoken promises, He now gives you a special pledge or guarantee of His forgiving love. It is nothing less than His own body and blood. We are familiar with the use of pledges. The wedding ring is a "pledge and token of wedded love and faithfulness." The precious body and blood of your Lord in the Sacrament is to be for you and all disciples until the end of time the unfailing token and pledge of His saving love. Then, too, as you personally receive the bread and the wine with your mouth, you understand more fully your Savior's words, "given and shed *for you*, for the remission of sins." In this Holy Supper, then, you have His boundless forgiveness *individualized* and *personalized*. It would mean little to you to know in an abstract way that God is

Love. But it means everything to you to know that God loves *you,* that *you,* personally, sinner though you are, are the object and recipient of His saving love tonight.

The words, "This is My body, which is given for you . . . this is My blood, shed for you," also tell you that there is in this Supper a most blessed *communion* between you and your Lord and between you and your fellow communicants in the Lord. The Lord of heaven comes to you, is with you, in the eating and drinking of the earthly elements. "The cup of blessing which we bless, is it not the communion of the blood of Christ? The bread which we break, is it not the communion of the body of Christ?" says the Apostle Paul (1 Cor. 10:16). Christ gives you this communion for the strengthening of your faith in the forgiveness of your sins and for the furtherance of your Christian life. Therewith He also reinforces His great promise, "Lo, I am with you alway, even unto the end of the world." (Matt. 28:20)

This blessed communion is yours because He had you in mind when He gave His Holy Supper.

III

Feast with your Lord again this evening and receive His blessings anew!

Many years have passed since that first Maundy Thursday, when the first disciples ate of that heavenly supper with their Lord. Since that time countless Christians throughout the ages have received the comfort and strength of this Holy Communion with their Lord and with each other in their own day. The Upper Room is ever a present-day room to the believer. When Leonardo da Vinci painted the *Last Supper,* he placed that incident from the life of our Lord into a contemporary setting. Under the magic of his brush, the Upper Room becomes an Italian dining hall. The Master and His disciples take their places at a Renaissance table. Tonight, as we are gathered here to eat and to drink with Him, this twentieth-century church is transformed into the Upper Room. The same Host is here. Disciples are here. You are among them. You hear His words, "This is My body, which is given for you. . . . My blood, which is shed for you. . . ."

For you! How grateful you should be for those words! We acknowledge and confess our sins and shortcomings as God's children. You know best what your sins are, as a parent, a neighbor, a son or daughter, a student, an employer, an employee. If it were not for the earnest invitation of your Lord and His precious promise of pardon and peace in this Sacrament, you might well hesitate to come before Him, for fear that a just and holy God might turn His face from you. But can you doubt the words of Him who gave His own body and shed His own blood to make all things right for you with God? Must not your grateful heart sing with St. Paul, "Therefore being justified by faith, we have peace with God through our Lord Jesus Christ; by whom also we have access by faith into this grace wherein we stand, and rejoice in hope of the glory of God" (Rom. 5:1-2). Again, "For ye have not received the spirit of bondage again to fear; but ye have received the Spirit of adoption, whereby we cry, Abba, Father. The Spirit itself beareth witness with our spirit, that we are the children of God: and if children, then heirs; heirs of God, and joint heirs with Christ." (Rom. 8:15-17)

One of the bitter experiences of life is the experience of being rejected. One can take many kinds of blows, but to be rejected by one's fellow men is indeed staggering. It is something for which no amount of money or influence or education can compensate. You are a social being, created so by God. Acceptance by your fellow man is vital to your happiness. But much more important — no, all-important is your acceptance by God. There is no anguish more haunting than the feeling of being rejected by God. For that, my friends, is hell!

Jesus, your Lord, experienced both rejections. He was despised and rejected by men. He was forsaken by God. But it was precisely through His terrible rejection that you are accepted. Never need you be haunted by the tormenting thought that God does not want you.

You were there in His thoughts when He gave His Holy Supper. Thank and praise Him all your days for that. For the solid bedrock of your hope and joy are these words: "This is My body which is given for *you*. . . . This cup is the new testament in My blood, which is shed for *you*. . . . This do in remembrance of Me." Amen.

WERE YOU THERE

When He Was Laid in the Tomb?

And after this Joseph of Arimathea, being a disciple of Jesus, but secretly for fear of the Jews, besought Pilate that he might take away the body of Jesus; and Pilate gave him leave. He came therefore, and took the body of Jesus. And there came also Nicodemus, which at the first came to Jesus by night, and brought a mixture of myrrh and aloes, about an hundred pound weight. Then took they the body of Jesus, and wound it in linen clothes with the spices, as the manner of the Jews is to bury. Now in the place where He was crucified there was a garden; and in the garden a new sepulcher, wherein was never man yet laid. There laid they Jesus therefore because of the Jews' preparation day; for the sepulcher was nigh at hand. — John 19:38-42.

How does one go about describing that tremendous moment in history when the Son of God died on the cross for the sin of the world?

Perhaps it were better for us not to attempt any such thing, better simply to turn to the plain and reverent language of the inspired record: "And when Jesus had cried with a loud voice, He said, Father, into Thy hands I commend My spirit; and having said thus, He gave up the ghost." (Luke 23:46)

All was finished now — not only His suffering of the last few hours, but everything He had come to do. It began in God's heart in eternity. It began on earth in the manger, on a silent starlit night, the night the angel told the shepherds — and the world, "Fear not; for, behold, I bring you good tidings of great joy, which shall be to all people. For unto you is born this day in the city of David a Savior, which is Christ the Lord." Strangely enough, it was gloriously completed on a cross — the work of man's redemption — on a day as dark as night. No angel voices are heard here. Only His voice. It is fitting that He, the dying yet triumphant Son of God, Himself should make the announcement of His victory: "It is finished!" (John 19:30)

His soul now rested in His Father's hands. His bruised and lifeless body still remained on the cross. The leaders insisted that the bodies be removed before the Sabbath, which was a high day. It would not be a pretty sight for the pilgrims and visitors who had overflowed Jerusalem for the Passover. So the legs of the two thieves were clubbed to hasten their death. But this was not necessary in Jesus' case. He was already dead. To make sure, a soldier jabbed a spear into His side. But the Lord had by an act of His will laid down His life, as He had foretold. Now, what would happen to His body? This was the question that must have filled the already tortured minds of that loyal little band standing beneath the cross. We can perhaps feel something of their anxiety at a time like this.

An understanding God has preserved for us in the Sacred Record a moving and thoroughly human story of the burial of our Lord. It is the story of loving hands that gently laid to rest His pierced and pallid body. The artist Rubens and others have endeavored to recapture on canvas the moment of the descent from the cross. It is a picture of outstretched hands, willing and helpful hands, which received His body and bore it to the tomb. But many other people were there who could not possibly be included in such a picture — for example, you and I.

WERE YOU THERE WHEN HE WAS LAID IN THE TOMB?

I

There is Joseph of Arimathea, a respected and well-to-do man. Joseph was a member of the Jewish council, the Sanhedrin, which had condemned Jesus to death, but he had not consented to the deed. He was a devout man, waiting for the appearance of the Messiah. In fact, he was a disciple of Jesus, but "secretly for fear of the Jews" (v. 38). Somehow he has overcome his fear and now goes boldly to Pilate to ask for the body of Jesus. He wants to give His body a decent burial in his own family tomb, a new tomb, where nobody had yet been laid. Having received the governor's permission, Joseph saw to it that the body of Jesus was removed from the cross. Now, all this was a public confession on the part of Joseph as to his relation to the crucified One. By this action he threw off the cloak of secrecy. He was willing to stand up and be counted. And what a joy this must have been for the brave women and that disciple John, who out of love for their crucified Lord had faced the abuse and scorn of the mob alone. Through this new ally their Lord's body would be reverently cared for and given honorable burial.

Then there is Nicodemus, another member of the Sanhedrin. You will recognize him as the one who came to Jesus by night because he was either ashamed or afraid to be seen in the company of the Nazarene. That was a memorable visit — perhaps there had been others — when he learned from Jesus the true nature of the kingdom of God and how to enter it: "Except a man be born of water and of the Spirit, he cannot enter into the kingdom of God. That which is born of the flesh is flesh; and that which is born of the Spirit is spirit. Marvel not that I said unto thee, Ye must be born again" (John 3:5-7). Certainly Nicodemus had not consented to the death of Jesus; perhaps he had not been present when He was condemned. At any rate, he cannot remain a secret disciple any longer. Nicodemus now comes out into the open. He approaches the garden tomb, bringing a supply of costly spices, a mixture of myrrh and aloes, for embalming the body. Again, what joy his coming must have brought to the friends of Jesus, as they now saw that in the end their Lord would receive a decent burial.

Is there anything we can learn from these men? Certainly not from their former fear, which caused them to hide their light under a bushel. But there is something here for those who faithfully "stand beneath the cross," in the thick of things alone. Sometimes they may get to feel like Elijah of old, lonely and beaten. It seemed to him that everyone in Israel, man, woman, and child, had forsaken God and had turned to worship Baal. In his disouragement he lamented to God, "I, even I only, am left" (1 Kings 19:14). That was probably true so far as Elijah could see at the moment. But God, the Searcher of hearts, reminded His dejected servant that He had yet seven thousand in Israel who had not bowed the knee to Baal. Elijah saw only himself; God discerned thousands of others. Yes, the church of God is much, much bigger than we sometimes think. The seven thousand in Israel and the Josephs and the Nicodemuses remind us of that today. Remind us that there is a church in Red China, that there is a church in Soviet Russia, in the hearts in which the Crucified dwells. Remind us of the lines from the mission hymn:

> Who dare not yet the faith avow,
> Tho' secretly they hold it now.

Remind us that God, at His hour, can embolden all of them to step forth and confess Him openly before the world.

II

The once timid Joseph and Nicodemus come forward to join the others who had stood beneath the cross — drawn together in the world by that cross. Together their hands prepare the body of their Lord. See them gently lift the body and carry it into Joseph's tomb and then roll a heavy stone before the entrance.

Yet not their hands alone laid Him in the tomb. Their hands were the hands of the world — your hands and my hands. We, too, helped lay Him there. It was our sin that laid Him, God's incarnate Son, into the grave. You need but recall that for His own sake God's Son had no need to suffer and to die and be buried. You must know, therefore, that in all this He was taking the place of others, acting as their Substitute. This is stated many times and in many ways in the Scripture. Thus Paul writes to the Colossian Christians: "And you, that were sometime alienated and enemies [of God] in your mind by wicked works, yet now hath He reconciled in the body of His flesh through death, to present you holy and unblamable and unreprovable in His sight" (Col. 1:21, 22). He could do this because He, the Son of God, also became one of us and lived among us. He lived a life of perfect obedience to God's holy will. We had transgressed that will and deserved to die. He took upon Himself our punishment, died for us, made an atonement for us.

So, then, we face this startling paradox: we say that we helped to lay Christ in Joseph's tomb, and we say that at the same time we were carried into the tomb with Him. Both statements are gloriously true. How so? Our sin, for which He died, put Him there. And since it was our sin which He took with Him into the tomb, we also went in with Him. When the stone was sealed on Him, it was also sealed on us. This is what St. Paul was talking about when he wrote to the Christians in Rome: "We are buried with Him." Indeed, it is only "if we have been planted together in the likeness of His death" that we can come forth again and "be also in the likeness of His resurrection." (Rom. 6:4, 5)

Our Lord's burial is significant, furthermore, because it is another confirmation of His death for us. Again, His burial fulfills a pointed prophecy of Isaiah in connection with the Messiah's death, namely, "He made His grave with the wicked, and with the rich in His death" (Is. 53:9). Thus even in the point of the burial of our Lord we find the evidence of divine direction. Finally, His burial marks the last stage in His state of humiliation before His glorious exaltation on the third day.

III

It is of the utmost personal importance for you to understand that you were there when they laid Him in the tomb, that your sins were buried with

Him. For to know and gratefully accept what He has done for you means to share in the eternal blessings of His death and resurrection. To those who are in fellowship with Him the grave becomes something quite new. It is not an end, but a beginning; not a blank wall, but an open door.

So it is that when we stand at the tomb of a fellow believer, a loved one, we know the grief and sorrow that all must feel at such a time, but with a tremendous difference. It is that difference which Christ alone makes, the difference expressed in the immortal words of St. Paul, "I would not have you to be ignorant, brethren, concerning them which are asleep, that ye sorrow not, even as others which have no hope. For if we believe that Jesus died and rose again, even so them also which sleep in Jesus will God bring with Him." (1 Thess. 4:13, 14)

Not all who die are buried by loving hands. The victims of war, of concentration camps and purges, are often literally "plowed under" with a terrible machinelike precision. Yet it is really not important what the hands of man may do for or to our lifeless forms. What matters is what Christ did for us when He once shared the grave with us.

Some graves in this vast cemetery of the earth bear no identification. No man knows who rests there. In Arlington National Cemetery is the well-known Tomb of the Unknown Soldier. This monument is a symbol of all the unknown dead. But they are unknown only to us. God knows them — each one of them. And the Good Shepherd who gave His life for the sheep reminds us: "I know my sheep . . . and I give unto them eternal life; and they shall never perish, neither shall any man pluck them out of my hand." (John 10:27, 28)

Yes, this is why He died for us. This is why He hallowed the grave for us. This then, is the mighty affirmation of Good Friday: "O death, where is thy sting? O grave, where is thy victory? . . . Thanks be to God, which giveth us the victory through our Lord Jesus Christ" (1 Cor. 15:55, 57). This alone is what makes it a *Good* Friday for us. Amen.

WERE YOU THERE

When He Rose from the Grave?

Therefore we are buried with Him by baptism into death: that like as Christ was raised up from the dead by the glory of the Father, even so we also should walk in newness of life. For if we have been planted together in the likeness of His death, we shall be also in the likeness of His resurrection.

Romans 6:4-5

We take our place this morning with millions of worshipers the world over, from the historic Holy Land to the colorful Grand Canyon. We have come together to celebrate the decisive victory of our Lord over death and the grave. By this we mean that Jesus Christ, the Son of God, who was crucified under Pontius Pilate, whose lifeless body was sealed in Joseph's tomb, on the third day snapped the bonds of death and rose victoriously from the grave.

Of all the events in the life of our Lord, His glorious resurrection is undoubtedly the one we should like most to have witnessed. What an overwhelming experience it would have been to stand before the empty tomb, to hear the angel's message, to talk with those Roman guards!

There is, however, a greater privilege than that of having been present at the resurrection as a mere spectator. It is the privilege of having been involved in the resurrection as a participant and beneficiary. But is such a thing possible? What do you think?

WERE YOU THERE WHEN HE ROSE FROM THE GRAVE?

Remember, Christ was your heaven-sent Substitute. The text tells you that when on Good Friday He died for your sins, it was as though you had died. When on Easter morning He victoriously rose from the grave, it was as if you had risen to life again. The text reminds you that through your Baptism you participate in the death and resurrection of your Lord and share in their great blessings. In Christ you were there!

Consider this morning the deep personal significance this Easter truth holds for you.

I

The resurrection affirms and confirms the deity of your Lord.

Jesus on numerous occasions had predicted His death on the cross. What is more significant is the fact that He likewise foretold His resurrection. He said not only, "The Son of Man shall be betrayed . . . and crucified," but also, "The third day He shall rise again." No mere mortal could seriously make such a claim. God alone has the power over death. God alone is the Source of life, yes, is Life. When Jesus asserted that He would rise from the grave, He was claiming for Himself the power over death, the possession of life itself. He was claiming to be God. And when He burst forth alive from the tomb, He proved it.

Do not permit any Easter pageantry or music or oratory to becloud this first great affirmation of the resurrection, namely, that it was God Himself who burst forth from the darkness of Joseph's tomb that first Easter day.

This is a tremendous affirmation. It means that the resurrected Christ is the Truth — "the Way, the Truth, and the Life." It means He is the omnipotent Lord of life and death. "Christ hath abolished death, and hath brought life and immortality to light through the Gospel."

Friend, are you one who feels that he has been mocked in his search for the truth? Are you disillusioned and cynical because you have come to feel that life really has no meaning? Let me remind you once again, in the light of the resurrection, of the Savior's familiar words, "Come unto Me, all ye that labor and are heavy laden, and I will give you rest. Take My yoke upon you, and learn of Me; for I am meek and lowly in heart; and ye shall find rest unto your souls." If on this Easter morning some disturbing problem of everyday living is robbing you of your joy, remember His words, "Seek ye first the kingdom of God and His righteousness, and all these things shall be added unto you." You've heard these words many times. But this morning I ask you to consider them in the resplendent light of Easter. Behind those words is not merely a kindly teacher, but the Son of God who showed to the world His truth and His power when He broke forth from the tomb. What we need most today is not more admiration of Jesus Christ, but *adoration* of this Christ as the Son of God, the Source of all truth and power. We need a day-by-day faith in His promises to help.

Faith is the grasping of Almighty Power,
The hand of man laid on the arm of God;
That grand and blessed hour
In which the things impossible to me
Become the possible, O Lord, through Thee.

Victorious living is possible for those who are risen with Christ. It is part of that glorious walking "in newness of life."

II

The second great affirmation of the resurrection is that of your complete redemption from sin by your victorious Lord.

Man needed desperately to be redeemed because he had sinned against God. Sin is a dreadful reality. If you believe in God, you must believe in sin; for "sin is the transgression of the law" of God. You

72

cannot eliminate sin from your life by denying it or "soft-pedaling" it. "A well-known preacher was once taken to task by one of his hearers for preaching a pointed sermon on sin. His well-meaning critic stated that if people heard so much about sin they would become sinners. The preacher took a bottle marked 'poison' from a shelf. 'I see what you want me to do,' he said. 'You want me to change the label. Suppose I take off this label and put on a mild label, like "essence of peppermint." Do you see what happens? The milder you make the label, the more dangerous you make the poison.'"

Sin is so dangerous because it alienates you from your God. You cannot live apart from God. "The wages of sin is death!" (Rom. 6:23). "By one man sin entered into the world, and death by sin; and so death passed upon all men, for that all have sinned." (Rom. 5:12)

Sin is so dangerous because it alienates you from your fellow man. Sin keeps you from composing your differences with others. In war as well as in your more personal relationships, the destructive and corrosive nature of pride, jealousy, duplicity, suspicion, hatred, and moral ignorance plays the major role, but is not fully recognized.

Now, the central message of the cross is that Jesus Christ, the Son of God, suffered and died in behalf of the sinful human race. He was your God-sent Substitute who took your guilt upon Himself, who suffered to pay the penalty of your sin. On the cross, when His work of redemption was complete,

He cried out, "It is finished!" But was it finished? Would His death suffice for us? Did He accomplish our redemption before God? During the dark hours between that Black Friday and that first Easter day, these questions remained unanswered. Then, on the first day of the week the answer came in a flashing, blinding light, bursting from the tomb upon the world: "He is risen!"

That is the victory in which you share. Listen, Paul tells the believers at Rome, and all believers: "We are buried with Him by Baptism into death: that like as Christ was raised up from the dead by the glory of the Father, even so we also should walk in newness of life."

"O death, where is thy sting? O grave, where is thy victory? The sting of death is sin; and the strength of sin is the Law. But thanks be to God, which giveth us the victory through our Lord Jesus Christ" (1 Cor. 15:55-57). Yes, God says to you through the resurrection of His Son: "Be sure, My child, your redemption from sin and death and hell is complete."

Accept your redemption from His holy hands. Thus you enter into new life with Him and "know the power of His resurrection" in your life. This is a transforming power. Every Christian has experienced it. It is freedom from an accusing conscience once at war with God. It is assurance of peace with God in Christ, that peace "which passeth all understanding." It is not the release from the suffering, the pain, and the sorrows of life. But it is the resource with which to face them, endure them, in a victorious way. Here is power also — in the forgiving love of God — to better our relationships with one another in our everyday lives. I am sure you will agree, for example, that a husband and wife who have taken the Christ of Easter into their hearts by faith and who regularly pray together for His daily blessing will have a much happier home life. I am also sure that those who sincerely pray His Prayer, including "forgive us our trespasses, as we forgive those who trespass against us," are not likely to harbor bitterness and resentment — things which so often disturb relationships at home, at work, at school, in the neighborhood, and even in the congregation.

Open your heart so that the cleansing and ennobling light of the resurrection may shine in with a newer brilliance. It is the Lord's earnest desire that you live in the light of your assured redemption, that you "walk in newness of life."

III

Now, as you look once more toward the empty tomb, the third great affirmation of the resurrection of your Lord is brought home to you: the resurrection of your body through Him. Paul says in the text: "For if we have been planted together in the likeness of His death, we shall be also in the likeness of His resurrection." (V. 5)

The idea of the continuation of life after death is nothing new. The pagans, among them Socrates and

Plato, believed in existence beyond the grave. The disciples of Jesus, crushed in spirit as they were, presumably had no doubts concerning their Master's immortality. But the resurrection of the body is a distinctive doctrine of the Christian religion. Jesus often referred to the subject. Once He said, "This is the will of Him that sent Me, that everyone which seeth the Son, and believeth on Him, may have everlasting life, and I will raise him up at the last day" (John 6:40). Later, St. Paul, referring to the resurrection of the body, wrote to the Thessalonians: "But I would not have you to be ignorant, brethren, concerning them which are asleep, that ye sorrow not, even as others which have no hope. For if we believe that Jesus died and rose again, even so them also which sleep in Jesus will God bring with Him." (1 Thess. 4:13, 14)

All this, again, has substance and meaning only because of the actual resurrection of our Lord from the dead. In Him you have more than the promise of an uncertain existence in some shadowy spirit world. In Him you have the certainty of personal and bodily identity beyond the grave. This is also the basis of the comforting Christian hope of the recognition of loved ones in His Kingdom of Glory.

Life in His kingdom must begin here and now for you. In fact, you must possess it now, if you are to enjoy it in its fullness when He comes again. This should not be surprising. For in Him the here and the hereafter are joined in an unbroken, never-ending present. God wants you to enter His kingdom now through faith in the risen Savior. That is why He has given you Easter with its great affirmations: the deity of your Lord, your complete redemption by your Lord, and your bodily resurrection through your Lord.

The angel's message is once more resounding through the world: "He is not here; he is risen!" By Holy Baptism you were there when He rose from the grave. You now have the assurance that you will also be there when He returns in glory. Therefore, lift up your voice with all the redeemed in the mighty, swelling chorus, "Thanks be to God which giveth us the victory through our Lord Jesus Christ!"

But, friend, now that you have all this, what are you going to do with it? Amen.

JAMES STEVENSON

What's Under My Bed

A MULBERRY PAPERBACK BOOK, New York

First Mulberry Edition, 1990
10 9 8 7 6 5 4

Library of Congress Cataloging in Publication Data

Stevenson, James [date]
What's under my bed?
Summary: Grandpa tells his two young houseguests
a story about his own childhood when he was
scared at bedtime.
[1. Bedtime—Fiction.   2. Grandfathers—Fiction.
3. Fear—Fiction] I. Title.
PZ7.S84748Wh   1983   [E]   83-1454
ISBN 0-688-09350-7

"Time for bed," said Grandpa. "I hope
that story wasn't too scary for you."
"Oh, no," said Mary Ann.
"Not for us," said Louie.

"Sleep well," said Grandpa.

"Would you leave the door open a little?" said Mary Ann.

"Or a lot?" said Louie.

"Certainly," said Grandpa. "Good night."

"I didn't believe that story, did you?" said Mary Ann.
"Of course not," said Louie. "Especially the monster part."
"And the screaming part," said Mary Ann.

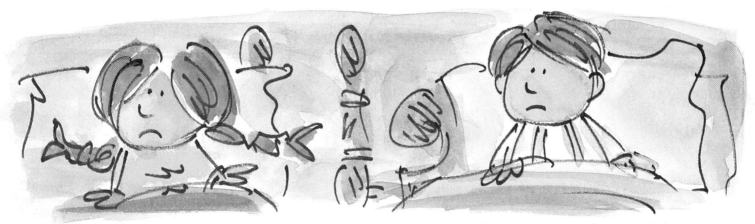

"Do you hear something?" asked Mary Ann, a few minutes later.
"Like what?" said Louie.
"Like something coming up the stairs," said Mary Ann.
"It's nothing," said Louie.

"Look at that shadow on the wall,"
said Mary Ann. "Here it comes."

"It's getting bigger," said Louie.
The door opened wide.

It was only Leonard, wagging his tail.

For a while it was quiet.
Then Mary Ann said,
"I think there's something
under my bed."

"There's nothing under your bed,"
said Louie.
"How do you know?"
said Mary Ann.

"I just know," said Louie.
"Take a look," said Mary Ann.
"I'm too tired," said Louie.

"I bet you're afraid to put your feet
over the edge," said Mary Ann.
"No, I'm not," said Louie.
He started to get out of bed.

Louie stepped on Leonard.
Leonard jumped and howled.
Mary Ann yelled.

Then they all ran downstairs.

"Well, hello," said Grandpa. "What seems to be the trouble?"
"Something was under our beds," said Mary Ann.
"Is that so?" said Grandpa.
"Why, the very same thing happened to me once.

It was long ago, when I was visiting my grandparents.
I was about your age. The house was strange.
I was a little bit scared on my way to bed.

As I went up the stairs, glittery eyes
stared at me through the window..."

"Those were probably just
fireflies, Grandpa," said Louie.
"Perhaps you're right,"
said Grandpa.

"My room was at the end of a long, long hall.

I went into my room, put on my pajamas,

picked up a book and read for a while.

Suddenly, I realized I had
forgotten to look under
the bed. I worked up my
nerve and took a peek.

It was awful! A creature
with wild hair, no head, and a long tail
was standing there.''

"But, Grandpa," said Mary Ann, "wasn't that your shoes and your bathrobe and your hairbrush, just where you had left them?" "Why, that's *just* what it was," said Grandpa.

"I got back into bed.

Then I heard some horrible sounds…little creatures on stilts.
They went *Gnik gnok*."

"Grandpa, was there a big grandfather
clock in the hall?" said Mary Ann.
"Why, yes, there was," said Grandpa.
"What did it sound like?" said
Mary Ann.
"Oh," said Grandpa. "I see what
you mean.

"Probably not a big bird,
Grandpa," said Louie.
"No?" said Grandpa. "Then
what could it have been?"
"A few moths," said Louie.

I closed my eyes. A huge and terrible bird
flew in. I could feel its feathers on my face."

"Just what it was,"
said Grandpa.

"Probably some cats jumping on garbage cans," said Mary Ann. "Probably," said Grandpa.

"But then, outside my window I heard pirates fighting with swords...*clash, clash!*"

"Then the bats came in. I could hear them fluttering all around me."

"Wait," said Louie.
"Yes?" said Grandpa.
"Could it have been the wind fluttering the pages of your book?" said Louie.
"Not only could have been," said Grandpa. "It was."

"You should have closed the window," said Mary Ann.
"Just what I did," said Grandpa.
"All quiet after that?" asked Louie.
"Yes," said Grandpa.

"Until the ghosts started wailing and moaning."

"You should have shut the window tighter," said Mary Ann.
"Right you are!" said Grandpa.
"I got up and shut the window tighter."

"Safe at last, eh?" said Louie.
"I *thought* so," said Grandpa.

"Were you scared, Grandpa?"
said Mary Ann.
"Indeed I was," said Grandpa.
"You shouldn't have been,"
said Mary Ann. "It was
the branches of the tree,
creaking in the wind."
"How did you know?" said
Grandpa.

"But then I heard the skeletons climbing up the side of
the house. Their bones were creaking as they climbed."

"Well, it was getting hot so I foolishly opened the window again."

"Not a good idea?" said Louie.
"No," said Grandpa. "The light blew out."
"Were you scared in the dark, Grandpa?" said Mary Ann.
"Just until I got used to it," said Grandpa.
"Then you felt better?" said Louie.

"No, worse," said Grandpa. "Then I could see
what was coming in the window."
"Such as?" said Mary Ann.
"Oh," said Grandpa,

"goblins, witches, spiders, giants,
    monsters, dragons, slitherers, and creepers,
    leeches that wriggled, wretches that giggled,

peaches that screeched, creatures that reached and
pinched and poked, nibbled and dribbled,
snapped and stomped and squished,

scratchers and catchers, growlers and howlers,
things that were smelly, or shaky like jelly!

Suddenly, they all started chasing *me*!
I ran out the door.

I could hear something coming after me.
I ran from one room to another, and down the halls.

I ran upstairs and down. Finally,

I stopped to rest.
I looked behind me.
Nothing was there.''

"Why it was only my grandpa and grandma.

They thought
maybe I was hungry.

They gave me a big bowl of strawberry ice cream.
I felt much better.''